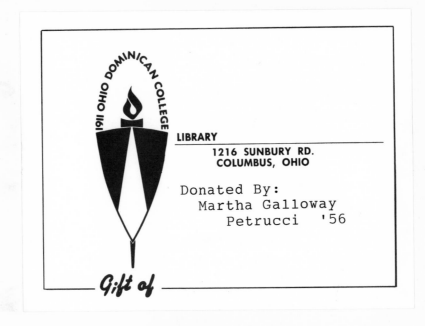

The Charge of the Light Brigade

Officers and Soldiers of
The Light Brigade in the Crimea

Alfred Lord Tennyson's
The Charge
of the
Light Brigade

ILLUSTRATED BY

Alice and Martin Provensen

GOLDEN PRESS · NEW YORK · AND · PAUL HAMLYN · LONDON

Library of Congress Card Number 64-18756

Published 1964 by Golden Press, Inc., New York
and
Paul Hamlyn, Ltd., Westbook House, Fulham Broadway, London
© Copyright 1964 by Golden Press, Inc.
Printed in the U.S.A.

The Charge of the Light Brigade
Commemorates the Disastrous
Cavalry Charge Against
the Russian Batteries
at Balaclava
October 25,

1854

I

Half a league, half a league,
Half a league onward,
All in the valley of Death
Rode the six hundred.

Into the valley of Death
Rode the six hundred.

II

"Forward, the Light Brigade!"
Was there a man dismay'd?
Not tho' the soldier knew
Some one had blunder'd.
Theirs not to make reply,
Theirs not to reason why,
Theirs but to do and die.
Into the valley of Death
Rode the six hundred.

III

Cannon to right of them,
Cannon to left of them,
Cannon in front of them
 Volley'd and thunder'd;
Storm'd at with shot and shell,
Boldly they rode and well,
Into the jaws of Death,
Into the mouth of hell
 Rode the six hundred.

IV

Flash'd all their sabres bare,
Flash'd as they turn'd in air
Sabring the gunners there,
Charging an army, while
All the world wonder'd.

Plunged in the battery-smoke
Right thro' the line they broke;
Cossack and Russian
Reel'd from the sabre-stroke
   Shatter'd and sunder'd.
Then they rode back, but not,
   Not the six hundred.

V

Cannon to right of them,
Cannon to left of them,
Cannon behind them
   Volley'd and thunder'd.

Storm'd at with shot and shell,
While horse and hero fell,
They that had fought so well
Came thro' the jaws of Death,
Back from the mouth of hell,
All that was left of them,
   Left of six hundred.

VI

When can their glory fade?
O the wild charge they made!
  All the world wonder'd.
Honor the charge they made!
Honor the Light Brigade,
  Noble six hundred.

1854

"C'est magnifique mais ce n'est pas la guerre."
…GENERAL BOSQUET

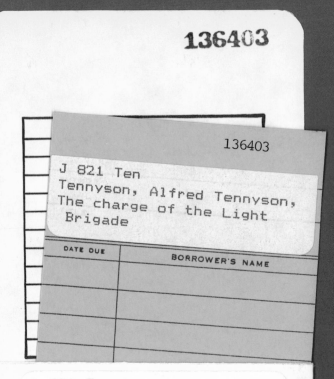